彩虹桥汉语分级读物
Rainbow Bridge Graded Chinese Reader

Starter: 150 vocabulary words

The Legend of Lantern Festival

元宵节的传说

叶婵娟 改编

MP3
Download Online
www.sinolingua.com.cn

华语教学出版社
SINOLINGUA

First Edition 2016

ISBN 978-7-5138-1063-0
Copyright 2016 by Sinolingua Co., Ltd
Published by Sinolingua Co., Ltd
24 Baiwanzhuang Road, Beijing 100037, China
Tel: (86) 10-68320585   68997826
Fax: (86) 10-68997826   68326333
http://www.sinolingua.com.cn
E-mail: hyjx@sinolingua.com.cn
Facebook: www.facebook.com/sinolingua
Printed by Beijing Jinghua Hucais Printing Co., Ltd

Printed in the People's Republic of China

编者的话

对于广大汉语学习者来说，要想快速提高汉语水平，扩大阅读量是很有必要的。"彩虹桥"汉语分级读物为汉语学习者提供了一系列有趣、有用的汉语阅读材料。本系列读物按照词汇量进行分级，并通过精彩的故事叙述，给读者带来了丰富有趣的阅读享受。本套读物主要有以下特点：

一、分级精准，循序渐进。我们参考了新汉语水平考试（HSK）词汇表（2012 年修订版）、《汉语国际教育用音节汉字词汇等级划分（国家标准）》和《常用汉语 1500 高频词语表》等词汇分级标准，结合《欧洲语言教学与评估框架性共同标准》（CEFR），设计了一套适合汉语学习者的"彩虹桥"词汇分级标准。本系列读物分为 7 个级别（入门级*、1 级、2 级、3 级、4 级、5 级、6 级），供不同水平的汉语学习者选择，每个级别故事的生词数量不超过本级别对应词汇量的 20%。随着级别的升高，故事的篇幅逐渐加长。本系列读物与 HSK、CEFR 的对应级别，各级词汇量以及每本书的字数详见下表。

---

* 入门级（Starter）在封底用 S 标识。

级别	入门级	1级	2级	3级	4级	5级	6级
对应级别	HSK1 CEFR A1	HSK1-2 CEFR A1-A2	HSK2-3 CEFR A2-B1	HSK3 CEFR A2-B1	HSK3-4 CEFR B1	HSK4 CEFR B1-B2	HSK5 CEFR B2-C1
词汇量	150	300	500	750	1 000	1 500	2 500
字数	1 000	2 500	5 000	7 500	10 000	15 000	25 000

二、**故事精彩，题材多样**。本套读物选材的标准就是"精彩"，所选的故事要么曲折离奇，要么感人至深，对读者构成奇妙的吸引力。选题广泛取材于中国的神话传说、民间故事、文学名著、名人传记和历史故事等，让汉语学习者在阅读中潜移默化地了解中国的文化和历史。

三、**结构合理，实用性强**。"彩虹桥"系列读物的每一本书中，除了中文故事正文之外，都配有主要人物的中英文介绍、生词英文注释及例句、故事正文的英文翻译、练习题以及生词表，方便读者阅读和理解故事内容，提升汉语阅读能力。练习题主要采用客观题，题型多样，难度适中，并附有参考答案，既可供汉语教师在课堂上教学使用，又可供汉语学习者进行自我水平检测。

如果您对本系列读物有什么想法，比如推荐精彩故事、提出改进意见等，请发邮件到 liuxiaolin@sinolingua.com.cn，与我们交流探讨。也可以关注我们的微信公众号 CHQRainbowBridge，随时与我们交流互动。同时，微信公众号会不定期发布有关"彩虹桥"的出版信息，以及汉语阅读、中国文化小知识等。

韩　颖　刘小琳

Preface

For students who study Chinese as a foreign language, it's crucial for them to enlarge the scope of their reading to improve their comprehension skills. The "Rainbow Bridge" Graded Chinese Reader series is designed to provide a collection of interesting and useful Chinese reading materials. This series grades each volume by its vocabulary level and brings the learners into every scene through vivid storytelling. The series has the following features:

I. A gradual approach by grading the volumes based on vocabulary levels. We have consulted the New HSK Vocabulary (2012 Revised Edition), the *Graded Chinese Syllables, Characters and Words for the Application of Teaching Chinese to the Speakers of Other Languages (National Standard)* and the 1500 Commonly Used High Frequency Chinese Vocabulary, along with the Common European Framework of Reference for Languages (CEFR) to design the "Rainbow Bridge" vocabulary grading standard. The series is divided into seven levels (Starter*, Level 1, Level 2, Level 3, Level 4, Level 5 and Level 6) for students at different stages in their Chinese education to choose from. For each level, new words are no more than 20% of the vocabulary amount as specified in the corresponding HSK and CEFR levels.

---

*   Represented by "S" on the back cover.

As the levels progress, the passage length will in turn increase. The following table indicates the corresponding "Rainbow Bridge" level, HSK and CEFR levels, the vocabulary amount, and number of characters.

Level	Starter	1	2	3	4	5	6
HSK/ CEFR Level	HSK1 CEFR A1	HSK1-2 CEFR A1-A2	HSK2-3 CEFR A2-B1	HSK3 CEFR A2-B1	HSK3-4 CEFR B1	HSK4 CEFR B1-B2	HSK5 CEFR B2-C1
Vocabulary	150	300	500	750	1000	1500	2500
Characters	1000	2500	5000	7500	10,000	15,000	25,000

II. Intriguing stories on various themes. The series features engaging stories known for their twists and turns as well as deeply touching plots. The readers will find it a joyful experience to read the stories. The topics are selected from Chinese mythology, legends, folklore, literary classics, biographies of renowned people and historical tales. Such widely ranged topics would exert an invisible, yet formative, influence on readers' understanding of Chinese culture and history.

III. Reasonably structured and easy to use. For each volume of the "Rainbow Bridge" series, apart from a Chinese story, we also provide an introduction to the main characters in Chinese and English, new words with English explanations and sample sentences, and an English translation of the story, followed by comprehension exercises and a vocabulary list to help users read and understand the story and improve their Chinese reading skills. The exercises are mainly presented as objective questions that take on various forms with moderate difficulty. Moreover, keys to the exercises are also provided. The series can be used by teachers in class or by students for self-study.

If you have any questions, comments or suggestions about the series, please email us at liuxiaolin@sinolingua.com.cn. You can also exchange ideas with us via our WeChat account: CHQRainbowBridge. This account will provide updates on the series along with Chinese reading materials and cultural tips.

Han Ying and Liu Xiaolin

主要人物和地点
Main Characters and Places

汉武帝（Hànwǔdì）：中国古代汉朝的一位皇帝，他把国家治理得很好。

Emperor Wu of the Han Dynasty: An emperor during the Han Dynasty (206 BC–220 AD) in ancient China who was a wise ruler.

东方朔（Dōngfāng Shuò）：汉武帝的一个大臣，非常聪明。

Dongfang Shuo: One of the cabinet ministers of Emperor Wu who was very intelligent.

宫　女（gōngnǚ）：皇宫里的侍女。

Palace maid: A maidservant in the imperial palace.

长　安（Cháng'ān）：汉朝的都城之一，是中国古代著名的大城市，也就是现在的西安。

Chang'an: One of the capital cities of the Han Dynasty, which is modern day Xi'an. Chang'an was a famous metropolis in ancient China.

元宵节① 的传说②

Yuan xiaojie de chuanshuo

汉武帝的时候，有个人叫东方朔。他是个很聪明③的人，汉武帝很喜欢他。

Han wǔ di de shí hou
you
de ren jiao Dong Fang shuò Ta shi ge
hen cōngming de ren
Han wu di
hen xihuan ta

↑

liked

① 元宵节 (Yuánxiāo Jié) *n.* Lantern Festival
e.g., 元宵节这一天，中国人要看花灯、吃元宵。

② 传说 (chuánshuō) *n.* legend
e.g., 中国古代有很多好玩的传说故事。

③ 聪明 (cōngmíng) *adj.* intelligent
e.g., 这个小男孩儿很聪明。

有一天，东方朔在皇宫①里，看见一个宫女②一边走一边哭。东方朔觉得③她一定有什么难事，就走在她后面。

① 皇宫 (huánggōng) *n.* imperial palace
e.g., 皇宫很大、很漂亮。

② 宫女 (gōngnǚ) *n.* palace maid
e.g., 皇宫里有很多宫女。

③ 觉得 (juéde) *v.* feel
e.g., 我觉得很热。

① 水井 (shuǐjǐng) *n.*
water well
e.g., 这里有一个水
井。

② 马上 (mǎshàng)
adv. immediately
e.g., 我马上就来，你
等我一会儿。

走到 水井① 旁边

宫女想要跳进去。东方

朔马上② 跑过去拉住她，

问："你有什么难事，为

什么要死？"

宫女哭着说："我来皇宫好几年了，一直[1]不能回家。前几天听人说，我妈妈因为想我，生病了。"

① 一直 (yìzhí) *adv.*
all along
e.g., 这么多年来，他一直坚持帮助那位老人。

　　"见不到我，妈妈的
病就好不了。我活着出
不了皇宫，不如死了，
还能叫妈妈看看我！"
说着，这个宫女又哭了
起来。

东方朔说："如果你死了，你妈妈见到你又有什么用？你不要哭了。我一定帮你出去，见见你的家人！"

① 东西 (dōngxi)
n. stuff
e.g., 你买了什么东西?

东方朔回到家里，就在屋子外面忙着把东西①拿来拿去，看起来很着急。

他的邻居①看见后，觉得很奇怪②，就问东方朔："你这是在干什么？"

① 邻居 (línjū)
n. neighbor
e.g., 他是我的邻居。

② 奇怪 (qíguài) *adj.*
surprised, confused
e.g., 好好的，她怎么哭了？真奇怪！

① 正月 (zhēngyuè) *n.*
first lunar month
e.g., 正月十五是元宵节。

② 火神 (Huǒ Shén) *n.*
Fire God

③ 烧 (shāo) *v.*
burn, set sth. on fire
e.g., 大火要把房子都烧完了。

④ 放 (fàng) *v.* put, place
e.g., 我把东西放在这里了。

东方朔 对邻居说:"正月①十五火神②会来烧③长安城,我想看看东西放④在哪里好。"

9

邻居听了，也很着急，跑回家收拾①东西去了。很快，长安城里的人们都知道了这件事。

① 收拾 (shōushi) v.
pack up, gather up
e.g., 你的东西收拾好了吗?

　　没过几天，<u>汉武帝</u>也听到了这件事。他找来<u>东方朔</u>，问："听说<u>火神</u>正月十五要来烧<u>长安城</u>，这怎么好？"

东方朔说："是的，
我也听说了。您^①要想
想办法^②，不能让^③火神
来烧我们。"

① 您 (nín) *pron.*
(respectful form)
you
e.g., 您好！

② 办法 (bànfǎ) *n.*
solution, idea
e.g., 我有一个好办
法。

③ 让 (ràng) *v.* let
e.g., 让我好好想一
想。

① 点 (diǎn) *v.*
light up
e.g., 停电了，快把蜡烛点上。

② 灯笼 (dēnglong)
n. lantern
e.g., 我家有一个大红灯笼。

③ 放 (fàng) *v.* set off
e.g., 春节到了，我们都要放鞭炮。

④ 烟火 (yānhuo)
n. fireworks
e.g., 夜空中的烟火真漂亮。

汉武帝问："你有什么好办法吗？"东方朔想了想，说："正月十五那天晚上，我们在长安城里点 ① 灯笼 ②，放 ③ 烟火 ④。"

<u>汉武帝</u>想了想，说："<u>火神</u>看到了，觉得这里已经<u>着火</u>①了，就不会烧<u>长安城</u>了。"

① 着火 (zháohuǒ) *v.*
catch a fire
e.g., 着火了，快跑！

东方朔说："您说得太对了！如果您同意这么去做，那我们大家就都要谢谢您！"

汉武帝笑了。他想了想又说："这个办法好是好。可是，如果火神知道了真相①，一定会很生气的。"

① 真相 (zhēnxiàng)
n. truth
e.g., 妈妈知道这件事的真相后，就不再生气了。

16

① 元宵 (yuánxiāo)
n. yuanxiao (sweet dumplings made of glutinous rice flour)
e.g., 我很喜欢吃元宵。

东方朔说："我听说火神喜欢吃元宵①。正月十五那一天，我们让宫女拿着元宵去皇宫外等着，如果火神知道了真相，就给他吃元宵，他就不会生气了。"

汉武帝听了很高兴，命令① 人们快去做灯笼和烟火，只等着正月十五晚上用。

① 命令 (mìnglìng) *v.*
order
e.g., 将军命令他今天就出发。

① 火光 (huǒguāng) *n.*
blaze, glaring light
e.g., 这么多火光，是
不是着火了?

到了正月十五这天晚上，<u>长安城</u>里点了很多灯笼，人们都在放烟火，走到哪里都是火光①。

汉武帝又让宫女们煮①了很多元宵。宫女们拿着元宵从皇宫里出来，很多人看见了自己几年没见的女儿②，都很高兴。

① 煮 (zhǔ) v. boil
e.g., 我煮了一碗面条。

② 女儿 (nǚ'ér) n. daughter
e.g., 他有一个女儿。

这个晚上，<u>长安城</u>真的没有被烧。<u>汉武帝</u>很高兴，就命令人们每年正月十五都点灯笼、放烟火、吃元宵。

后来，人们就把正月十五这天叫作"元宵节"。每到这一天，人们就会在外面点很多灯笼。

① 越来越 (yuè lái
yuè) more and more
e.g., 她越来越漂亮
了。

② 花灯 (huādēng) n.
colorful lantern
e.g., 正月十五看花
灯。

③ 热闹 (rènao)
adj. lively
e.g., 元宵节的晚上，
外面很热闹。

元宵节的灯笼做得越来越 ① 漂亮，叫作"花灯 ②"。每年元宵节晚上，人们吃元宵、放烟火、看花灯，很热闹 ③。

很多年轻①的男女会在元宵节这一天一起看花灯，所以，元宵节也是情人②们见面约会③的好日子。

① 年轻 (niánqīng)
adj. young
e.g., 妈妈还很年轻。

② 情人 (qíngrén) *n.*
lover
e.g., 他没有情人。

③ 约会 (yuēhuì) *v.*
have a date with
e.g., 他和女朋友今天在咖啡馆约会。

The Legend of Lantern Festival

During the reign of Emperor Wu of the Han Dynasty, there lived a very intelligent man named Dongfang Shuo. The emperor liked him very much.

One day, Dongfang saw a maid weeping while walking through the palace. Feeling that she must have run into some trouble, he decided to follow her.

The maid walked up to a well and was about to jump in. Dongfang ran to her immediately and pulled her back. He asked the maid, "What happened? Why are you trying to kill yourself?"

The maid said with tears in her eyes, "I've been in the palace for several years and I can't go home. I heard a few days ago that my mother had fallen ill because she missed me so much. My mom won't recover unless she sees me. Since I cannot go outside of the palace, I'd rather die so she will be able to see my body." She continued to weep after saying this.

Dongfang said, "If you were dead, what's the point of your mother seeing you? Stop crying and I shall help you get out and meet with your family!"

Upon returning home, Dongfang began moving his household stuff in the courtyard and appeared quite anxious.

His neighbor saw this and was confused. He asked, "What on

earth are you doing, Dongfang?"

He replied, "On the 15th day of the first lunar month, the Fire God will come and set the Chang'an City on fire. I'm looking now for a new, safe location for my stuff."

The neighbor started to worry when he learned this and rushed home to pack up his house stuff, too. Before long the message was known to everybody in the city.

Only a few days later, the emperor received the news. He called Dongfang in and asked, "I heard that the Fire God would show up on the 15th day of the first lunar month to burn the Chang'an City. What should we do then?"

Dongfang replied, "Yes, I've also heard about that. Your Majesty, please think of a solution lest the Fire God comes to burn us."

The emperor asked, "Do you have any solutions?" Dongfang thought for a while and said, "We can light up lanterns and set off fireworks in Chang'an that night."

The emperor pondered and then said, "When the Fire God sees the scene, he may think that there's already a fire here and won't come to burn our city."

Dongfang said, "Your Majesty, you are absolutely right! If you agree to do so, we shall all be grateful to you!"

The emperor smiled, but after a second thought, he said, "Although the solution is good, the Fire God would become very angry upon learning the truth."

Dongfang replied, "I heard that the Fire God likes to eat *yuanxiao*. On the 15th day of the first lunar month, we can ask the palace maids to carry some *yuanxiao* outside the palace and wait for him. If he learns the truth, just present him the food so that he won't get angry."

The emperor was very pleased to hear this idea and ordered the people to make lanterns and fireworks right away to prepare for that evening.

That evening came and there were many lanterns lit up throughout the city. People were setting off fireworks and every place was filled with glaring lights.

The emperor then asked the maids to boil lots of *yuanxiao*. As they went out of the palace with the food, many people became overjoyed because they met with their daughters whom they hadn't seen for several years.

That night, there was no fire in Chang'an. The emperor was delighted and thus ordered his people light up lanterns, set off fireworks and eat *yuanxiao* on the 15th of the first lunar month each year ever since.

Later, the 15th day of the first lunar month has been named the Lantern Festival, on which people light up a lot of lanterns outdoors.

The lanterns for the festival have been becoming more and more beautiful and are called 花灯 , or colorful festive lanterns. In the evening of every Lantern Festival, people will have a jolly time by eating *yuanxiao*, lighting fireworks and watching the festive lanterns.

Many young couples enjoy the colorful lanterns on this day, thus the Lantern Festival is also a good time for lovers to meet and go on a date.

一、朗读下面的短语。Read the following phrases.

yìbiān zǒu yìbiān kū　　nálái náqù　　juéde qíguài
一边 走 一边 哭　　拿来拿去　　觉得奇怪

shōushi dōngxi
收拾 东西

二、思考题。Pre-reading questions.

1. 元宵节是哪一天？

2. 元宵节的时候，人们都做些什么？

课后练习 Reading exercises

一、除了东方朔，还有两个人帮宫女走出皇宫、见到家人。他们知道自己帮了宫女吗？他们是谁？他们都做了什么？ Besides Dongfang Shuo, there were two other people who helped the maid get out the palace and meet her family, but were they aware that they had done her such a favor? Who were they and what did they do?

1. _____

2. _____

3. _____

二、为下列各题选择正确的答案。 Choose the correct answer according to the story.

1. 那个宫女一边走一边哭，因为（   ）。

   A. 她想见东方朔　　　　B. 她想见汉武帝

   C. 她想见她的妈妈　　　　D. 她想吃元宵

2. 东方朔回家后，把东西拿来拿去，因为（   ）。

   A. 火神会来烧长安城

   B. 想和邻居开玩笑

   C. 他要让人们知道，火神要烧长安城

   D. 想收拾东西

3. 正月十五晚上点灯笼、放烟火的办法是谁想的？（　　　）

　　A. 汉武帝　　　　　　　　B. 东方朔

　　C. 宫女　　　　　　　　　D. 邻居

4. 如果不点灯笼、放烟火，火神会来烧长安城吗？（　　　）

　　A. 会　　　　　　　　　　B. 不会

　　C. 可能会　　　　　　　　D. 有时候会

5. 以下哪项不是人们元宵节做的事？（　　　）

　　A. 吃元宵　　　　　　　　B. 放烟火

　　C. 看花灯　　　　　　　　D. 收拾东西

三、判断题：请根据故事内容判断下列说法是否正确，如果正确请标"T"，不正确请标"F"。
Decide whether the following statements are true (T) or false (F).

1. 宫女的妈妈生病了，她很想出宫去看妈妈。　　　　（　　　）

2. 东方朔很喜欢收拾东西。　　　　　　　　　　　　（　　　）

3. 东方朔说火神会来烧长安城，邻居觉得是真的。（　　　）

4. 汉武帝听说火神喜欢吃元宵。　　　　　　　　　　（　　　）

5. 元宵节也是情人们见面约会的好日子。　　　　　　（　　　）

1. 他的邻居看见后觉得很奇怪，就问东方朔："＿＿＿＿＿＿？"

2. 如果火神知道了真相，就给他吃元宵，＿＿＿＿＿＿＿。

3. 汉武帝听了很高兴，_____ 人们快去 _____。

4. 这个晚上，长安城真的 _____。

5. 很多年轻的男女会 _____ 一起看花灯。

课后练习答案 Keys to the exercises

一、除了东方朔，还有两个人帮宫女走出皇宫、见到家人。他们知道自己帮了宫女吗？他们是谁？他们都做了什么？

　1. 不知道。

　2. 东方朔的邻居，汉武帝

　3. 邻居告诉人们火神要来烧长安城；汉武帝同意东方朔想的办法，让宫女拿着元宵走出皇宫。

二、为下列各题选择正确的答案

　　1. C　2. C　3. B　4. B　5. D

三、判断题：请根据故事内容判断下列说法是否正确，如果正确请标"T"，不正确请标"F"

　　1. T　2. F　3. T　4. F　5. T

四、看图复述故事内容

　　1. 你这是在干什么

　　2. 如果　他就不会生气了

　　3. 命令　做灯笼和烟火

　　4. 没有被烧

　　5. 在元宵节这一天

词汇表
Vocabulary List

办法	bànfǎ	*n.*	solution, idea		情人	qíngrén	*n.*	lover
传说	chuánshuō	*n.*	legend		让	ràng	*v.*	let
聪明	cōngmíng	*adj.*	intelligent		热闹	rènao	*adj.*	lively
灯笼	dēnglong	*n.*	lantern		烧	shāo	*v.*	burn, set sth. on fire
点	diǎn	*v.*	light up					
东西	dōngxi	*n.*	stuff		收拾	shōushi	*v.*	pack up, gather up
放	fàng	*v.*	put, place					
放	fàng	*v.*	set off		水井	shuǐjǐng	*n.*	water well
宫女	gōngnǚ	*n.*	palace maid		烟火	yānhuo	*n.*	fireworks
花灯	huādēng	*n.*	colorful lantern		一直	yìzhí	*adv.*	all along
皇宫	huánggōng	*n.*	imperial palace		元宵	yuánxiāo	*n.*	yuanxiao (sweet dumplings made of glutinous rice flour)
火光	huǒguāng	*n.*	blaze, glaring light					
火神	Huǒ Shén	*n.*	Fire God		元宵节	Yuánxiāo Jié	*n.*	Lantern Festival
觉得	juéde	*v.*	feel		约会	yuēhuì	*v.*	have a date with
邻居	línjū	*n.*	neighbor					
马上	mǎshàng	*adv.*	immediately		越来越	yuè lái yuè		more and more
命令	mìnglìng	*v.*	order					
年轻	niánqīng	*adj.*	young		真相	zhēnxiàng	*n.*	truth
您	nín	*pron.*	(respectful form) you		正月	zhēngyuè	*n.*	first lunar month
女儿	nǚ'ér	*n.*	daughter		煮	zhǔ	*v.*	boil
奇怪	qíguài	*adj.*	surprised, confused		着火	zháohuǒ	*v.*	catch a fire

项目策划：韩　颖　刘小琳
责任编辑：韩　颖　彭　博
英文编辑：薛彧威
英文翻译：薛彧威
封面设计：E°T创意工作室

图书在版编目（CIP）数据

元宵节的传说：汉、英／叶婵娟改编．— 北京：华语教学
出版社，2016
（"彩虹桥"汉语分级读物．入门级：150 词）
ISBN 978-7-5138-1063-0

Ⅰ．①元… Ⅱ．①叶… Ⅲ．①汉语－对外汉语教学－语言读
物 Ⅳ．① H195.5

中国版本图书馆 CIP 数据核字（2015）第 263027 号

元宵节的传说

叶婵娟　改编

*

©华语教学出版社有限责任公司

华语教学出版社有限责任公司出版

（中国北京百万庄大街24号　邮政编码 100037）

电话：(86)10-68320585　68997826

传真：(86)10-68997826　68326333

网址：www.sinolingua.com.cn

电子信箱：hyjx@sinolingua.com.cn

新浪微博地址：http://weibo.com/sinolinguavip

北京京华虎彩印刷有限公司印刷

2016年（32开）第1版

2016年第1版第1次印刷

（汉英）

ISBN 978-7-5138-1063-0

定价：15.00元